A Teddy Horsle

The Wind

Teddy Horsley and th... ...ly ...

Based on John 3 and Acts 2

by Leslie J Francis and Nicola M Slee

Pictures by Phillip Vernon

The Bear facts:

The Teddy Horsley Bible Series is designed to build bridges between the young child's day-to-day experiences of the world and major biblical themes and stories. The series is a result of extensive research into the religious development of young children, and the authors' wide experience of educational work in schools and churches.

Both authors work in Church-related institutions of education. Nicola Slee is a freelance writer and educator based at Queen's College, Birmingham. Leslie Francis is Director of the Welsh National Centre for Religious Education and Professor of Pastoral Theology at the University of Wales, Bangor.

Published by:
National Christian Education Council
1020 Bristol Road
Selly Oak
Birmingham
B29 6LB

British Library Cataloguing in Publication Data:
A catalogue record for this book is available from the British Library.

Text © Leslie J Francis and Nicola M Slee 1983
Illustrations © Phillip Vernon 2001

Unless otherwise stated, quotations from the Bible are from the *Good News Bible*, published by the Bible Societies/Collins, © American Bible Society, New York, 1966, 1971, 1976, 1992, 1994.

First published 1989 by the Bible Society, Swindon
Reprinted 1990, 1995
Second edition 2001

ISBN 0-7197-1001-4
Printed by Herald Forms Group

It is a windy day,
and Teddy Horsley is a puzzled bear.

He opens his eyes to look for the wind,
and cannot see it.

But he sees the wind shake apples down,

turn washing inside out,

and blow paper along the street.

He stretches out his paws to touch the wind, and cannot feel it.

But he feels the wind push him along,

tug his kite into the sky,

and drive rain into his face.

He pricks up his ears to listen to the wind,
and cannot hear it.

But he hears the wind rattle dustbin lids,

slam doors shut,

and whistle through the trees.

Teddy Horsley knows that the wind is there,
all around him.

The church is celebrating Pentecost,
and Teddy Horsley is a puzzled bear.

He opens his eyes to look for the Holy Spirit,
and cannot see it.

But he sees the Holy Spirit
making people smile and dance.

He stretches out his paws
to touch the Holy Spirit, and cannot feel it.

But he feels the Holy Spirit
making him safe and loved.

He pricks up his ears to listen to
the Holy Spirit, and cannot hear it.

But he hears the Holy Spirit
making people sing and laugh.

Teddy Horsley knows that
the Holy Spirit is there, all around him.

In *The Windy Day*, Teddy Horsley's experiences of trying to look for the wind, touch the wind, and listen to the wind help him to share in the Christian celebration of the Holy Spirit at Pentecost.

The wind blows wherever it wishes; you hear the sound it makes, but you do not know where it comes from or where it is going. It is like that with everyone who is born of the Spirit.

John 3.8

When the day of Pentecost came, all the believers were gathered together in one place. Suddenly there was a noise from the sky which sounded like a strong wind blowing, and it filled the whole house where they were sitting. Then they saw what looked like tongues of fire which spread out and touched each person there. They were all filled with the Holy Spirit.

Acts 2:1–4

The following questions suggest further ways of developing the links between the young child's experience, the story and the Bible passage.

Talk about the wind:

When have you been out on a windy day?
What did you see?
What did you feel?
What did you hear?

Talk about the story:

Why was Teddy Horsley a puzzled bear?
When he opened his eyes to look for the wind, what did he see?
When he stretched out his paws to touch the wind, what did he feel?
When he pricked up his ears to listen to the wind, what did he hear?
What did Teddy Horsley see, feel and hear in church at Pentecost?